Born in 1969, Madeleine Floyd studied
Fine Art and Illustration at Camberwell College
of Art, London, and has achieved great success in
both fields. Her illustrations, watercolours and oil
paintings are well known and have been published
and collected around the world. She works from
her garden studio in London and has become
one of Britain's best-loved artists. A long-standing
appreciation of nature led to Madeleine producing
a sketchbook full of Birdsong illustrations and this
has since grown into a successful range of beautiful
licensed products.

A Year of Birdsong

2020 Diary

" Tek - tek.... tek-tek ..." Tree Sparrow

Personal Details

Name

Address

Telephone: Home

Mobile

Work

E-mail

In emergency please contact:

Telephone

Useful Information

National Insurance no.

Driving licence no.

AA/RAC no.

Other Useful Numbers

Doctor	Dentist
Optician	Childminder
School	Vet
Bank	Building society
Train station	Bus station
Airport	Water
Plumber	Electrician
Gas	Electricity
Hairdresser	Garage
Taxi	Cinema

2020 Calendar

JANUARY
M	·	6	13	20	27
T	·	7	14	21	28
W	1	8	15	22	29
T	2	9	16	23	30
F	3	10	17	24	31
S	4	11	18	25	·
S	5	12	19	26	·

FEBRUARY
M	·	3	10	17	24
T	·	4	11	18	25
W	·	5	12	19	26
T	·	6	13	20	27
F	·	7	14	21	28
S	1	8	15	22	29
S	2	9	16	23	·

MARCH
M	30	2	9	16	23
T	31	3	10	17	24
W	·	4	11	18	25
T	·	5	12	19	26
F	·	6	13	20	27
S	·	7	14	21	28
S	1	8	15	22	29

APRIL
M	·	6	13	20	27
T	·	7	14	21	28
W	1	8	15	22	29
T	2	9	16	23	30
F	3	10	17	24	·
S	4	11	18	25	·
S	5	12	19	26	·

MAY
M	·	4	11	18	25
T	·	5	12	19	26
W	·	6	13	20	27
T	·	7	14	21	28
F	1	8	15	22	29
S	2	9	16	23	30
S	3	10	17	24	31

JUNE
M	1	8	15	22	29
T	2	9	16	23	30
W	3	10	17	24	·
T	4	11	18	25	·
F	5	12	19	26	·
S	6	13	20	27	·
S	7	14	21	28	·

JULY
M	·	6	13	20	27
T	·	7	14	21	28
W	1	8	15	22	29
T	2	9	16	23	30
F	3	10	17	24	31
S	4	11	18	25	·
S	5	12	19	26	·

AUGUST
M	31	3	10	17	24
T	·	4	11	18	25
W	·	5	12	19	26
T	·	6	13	20	27
F	·	7	14	21	28
S	1	8	15	22	29
S	2	9	16	23	30

SEPTEMBER
M	·	7	14	21	28
T	1	8	15	22	29
W	2	9	16	23	30
T	3	10	17	24	·
F	4	11	18	25	·
S	5	12	19	26	·
S	6	13	20	27	·

OCTOBER
M	·	5	12	19	26
T	·	6	13	20	27
W	·	7	14	21	28
T	1	8	15	22	29
F	2	9	16	23	30
S	3	10	17	24	31
S	4	11	18	25	·

NOVEMBER
M	30	2	9	16	23
T	·	3	10	17	24
W	·	4	11	18	25
T	·	5	12	19	26
F	·	6	13	20	27
S	·	7	14	21	28
S	1	8	15	22	29

DECEMBER
M	·	7	14	21	28
T	1	8	15	22	29
W	2	9	16	23	30
T	3	10	17	24	31
F	4	11	18	25	·
S	5	12	19	26	·
S	6	13	20	27	·

2021 Calendar

JANUARY
M	·	4	11	18	25
T	·	5	12	19	26
W	·	6	13	20	27
T	·	7	14	21	28
F	1	8	15	22	29
S	2	9	16	23	30
S	3	10	17	24	31

FEBRUARY
M	1	8	15	22	·
T	2	9	16	23	·
W	3	10	17	24	·
T	4	11	18	25	·
F	5	12	19	26	·
S	6	13	20	27	·
S	7	14	21	28	·

MARCH
M	1	8	15	22	29
T	2	9	16	23	30
W	3	10	17	24	31
T	4	11	18	25	·
F	5	12	19	26	·
S	6	13	20	27	·
S	7	14	21	28	·

APRIL
M	·	5	12	19	26
T	·	6	13	20	27
W	·	7	14	21	28
T	1	8	15	22	29
F	2	9	16	23	30
S	3	10	17	24	·
S	4	11	18	25	·

MAY
M	31	3	10	17	24
T	·	4	11	18	25
W	·	5	12	19	26
T	·	6	13	20	27
F	·	7	14	21	28
S	1	8	15	22	29
S	2	9	16	23	30

JUNE
M	·	7	14	21	28
T	1	8	15	22	29
W	2	9	16	23	30
T	3	10	17	24	·
F	4	11	18	25	·
S	5	12	19	26	·
S	6	13	20	27	·

JULY
M	·	5	12	19	26
T	·	6	13	20	27
W	·	7	14	21	28
T	1	8	15	22	29
F	2	9	16	23	30
S	3	10	17	24	31
S	4	11	18	25	·

AUGUST
M	30	2	9	16	23
T	31	3	10	17	24
W	·	4	11	18	25
T	·	5	12	19	26
F	·	6	13	20	27
S	·	7	14	21	28
S	1	8	15	22	29

SEPTEMBER
M	·	6	13	20	27
T	·	7	14	21	28
W	1	8	15	22	29
T	2	9	16	23	30
F	3	10	17	24	·
S	4	11	18	25	·
S	5	12	19	26	·

OCTOBER
M	·	4	11	18	25
T	·	5	12	19	26
W	·	6	13	20	27
T	·	7	14	21	28
F	1	8	15	22	29
S	2	9	16	23	30
S	3	10	17	24	31

NOVEMBER
M	1	8	15	22	29
T	2	9	16	23	30
W	3	10	17	24	·
T	4	11	18	25	·
F	5	12	19	26	·
S	6	13	20	27	·
S	7	14	21	28	·

DECEMBER
M	·	6	13	20	27
T	·	7	14	21	28
W	1	8	15	22	29
T	2	9	16	23	30
F	3	10	17	24	31
S	4	11	18	25	·
S	5	12	19	26	·

December 2019/January 2020

MONDAY
30

TUESDAY
31

New Year's Eve

WEDNESDAY
1

New Year's Day (Holiday UK, R. of Ireland, USA, CAN, AUS, NZL)

THURSDAY
2

Holiday (SCT, NZL)

FRIDAY
3

SATURDAY
4

SUNDAY
5

"Chek - chek - chek ...... chirrrr ....." Garden Warbler

Garden warbler *(Sylvia borin)*

Often praised as the virtuoso of the garden birds, the garden warbler is blessed with a remarkably musical and attractive song. Sometimes confused with the voice of the blackcap, this fellow appears to warble at length without drawing breath and produces an almost clarinet-like pure quality of tone that is loud, rich and brilliant.

Perhaps surprisingly, this musical maestro is rather plainly dressed in greyish brown plumage with dull buff underparts and was only identified at the end of the eighteenth century. He is less visible than one might expect from such an exuberant songster and builds his shallow nest in low thickets or fruit bushes that are adeptly concealed.

January

MONDAY
6

TUESDAY
7

WEDNESDAY
8

THURSDAY
9

FRIDAY
10

SATURDAY
11

SUNDAY
12

January

MONDAY
13

TUESDAY
14

WEDNESDAY
15

THURSDAY
16

FRIDAY
17

SATURDAY
18

SUNDAY
19

"Tzeee - tzeee ......" Crested Tit

NOTES

....

....

....

....

....

Crested tit *(Lophophanes cristatus)*

The crested tit can be found in pine forests and deciduous woods across mainland Europe and the Scottish Highlands in Great Britain. He is the proud owner of a tall, pointed, mottled, black and white head crest, which the male displays by spreading and closing his head crest feathers at times of courtship. This action is accompanied by a distinctive, if slightly stuttering, serenade and a number of endearing courtly bows to his female.

Seemingly oblivious or unconcerned by people, he can happily be watched at close distance. The male builds his nest often utilising a disused squirrel's drey or excavating his own soft, cup-shaped abode in a decaying tree stump.

January

Martin Luther King, Jr. Day (Holiday USA)

MONDAY
20

TUESDAY
21

WEDNESDAY
22

THURSDAY
23

FRIDAY
24

Burns Night (SCT)

SATURDAY
25

Australia Day (AUS)

SUNDAY
26

January/February

MONDAY
27

TUESDAY
28

WEDNESDAY
29

THURSDAY
30

FRIDAY
31

SATURDAY
1

SUNDAY
2

"Chip-chi-chirichirichiri"....Chaffinch

Chaffinch *(Fringilla coelebs)*

The loud, cheerful song of the chaffinch is a
welcome sign of a warmer season. The celebratory
melody accelerates downward and usually ends
with a wonderful flourish of notes before the song is
repeated up to ten times a minute. The male sings
loudly to mark out his breeding territory. With
his pinkish-orange chest and his blue bonnet, the
chaffinch enjoys woodland areas but is equally at
home in town or village gardens. The male brings
materials to the female for the nest, but it is the
female who actually builds a beautifully constructed
and compact nest in the fork of a tree using moss,
lichen and spiderwebs.

February

Waitangi Day (Holiday NZL)

February

MONDAY
10

TUESDAY
11

WEDNESDAY
12

THURSDAY
13

FRIDAY
14

St Valentine's Day

SATURDAY
15

SUNDAY
16

" Twit- twit... twit- twit...." Knot

NOTES

....

....

....

....

....

Knot *(Calidris canutus)*

The knot is a stocky, wading bird whose appearance
changes according to the seasons. In winter it is
grey, with a white belly, but in summer its chest
and face become brick red, almost like sunburn!
In America it is known as a red knot because of
this lovely summer plumage. Few sights can rival
that of the huge flocks that twist and turn in the
sky in winter as they visit the UK from their Arctic
breeding grounds; it has been estimated that some
of these wheeling flocks contain in excess of 100,000
birds. Knots have a short, deepish call, which fills
the air as they swoop and circle.

February

Presidents' Day (Holiday USA)

MONDAY
17

TUESDAY
18

WEDNESDAY
19

THURSDAY
20

FRIDAY
21

SATURDAY
22

SUNDAY
23

February/March

MONDAY
24

TUESDAY
25
Shrove Tuesday

WEDNESDAY
26
Ash Wednesday

THURSDAY
27

FRIDAY
28

SATURDAY
29

SUNDAY
1
St David's Day

"Kcaaaa - Kcaaaw............" Rook

NOTES

Rook *(Corvus frugilegus)*

The noisy cawing voice of this corvid (bird of the crow family) is raucous and resonant. Set at a similar pitch to that of a crying baby, it is an impossible call to miss.

This large bird flourishes in areas of mixed farming and is most often heard en masse, chatting voraciously as they build their breeding colony of nests high up in the bare winter branches. Glossy black in appearance, the rook is distinguished by his rather fluffy, thick black trouser feathers and the bare-faced patch at the base of his tapered bill.

March

MONDAY
2

TUESDAY
3

WEDNESDAY
4

THURSDAY
5

FRIDAY
6

SATURDAY
7

Daylight Saving Time begins (USA, CAN)

SUNDAY
8

March

MONDAY
9   Commonwealth Day

TUESDAY
10

WEDNESDAY
11

THURSDAY
12

FRIDAY
13

SATURDAY
14

SUNDAY
15

"Tsee-tsee-tsee-tsisitsisisisisi..." Blue Tit

Blue tit *(Cyanistes caeruleus)*

Sporting a blue cap and proud yellow chest, the blue tit is a much-loved visitor to the garden. His song is loud and high-pitched and ends in a long, rapid trill.

Swooping in to a sudden stop on the bird table, and often seen feeding upside down on peanut baskets, the bird's acrobatics and agility have earned our esteem. He can be found in gardens, parks and woodland. The female has similar plumage to the male and can lay up to 16 eggs in a single brood. Once the chicks have hatched, both parents work hard to keep their hungry offspring well fed with a constant supply of small caterpillars and other tasty morsels.

March

MONDAY
16

St Patrick's Day (Holiday N. Ireland, R. of Ireland)

TUESDAY
17

WEDNESDAY
18

THURSDAY
19

FRIDAY
20

SATURDAY
21

Mothering Sunday (UK, R. of Ireland)

SUNDAY
22

March

MONDAY
23

TUESDAY
24

WEDNESDAY
25

THURSDAY
26

FRIDAY
27

SATURDAY
28

SUNDAY
29

British Summer Time begins
European Daylight Saving Time begins

"Cuc-coo ... cuc-cooo .. " Cuckoo

NOTES

Cuckoo *(Cuculidae)*

From the middle of April, you can hear the
unmistakably melodious call of the male cuckoo.
His loud, rich and throaty song is unique,
reminiscent of a human mother affectionately
calling to her children, which perhaps explains
our love for him. Strangely, the female emits a
loud bubbling call after laying an egg or during
courtship. Even in Chaucer's time, the 'Cokkow'
was renowned for his fine anthem, and many old
customs involve the capture of a cuckoo in return
for an extension of good weather. Nevertheless, the
cuckoo's sweet crooning belies its incredibly anti-
social behaviour, as the female cuckoo roughly ousts
innocent songbird eggs from their nests, replacing
them with her own.

March/April

MONDAY
30

TUESDAY
31

WEDNESDAY
1

THURSDAY
2

FRIDAY
3

SATURDAY
4

Daylight Saving Time ends (NZL, AUS – except NT, QLD, WA)

SUNDAY
5

April

MONDAY
6

TUESDAY
7

WEDNESDAY
8

THURSDAY
9
First Day of Passover (Pesach)

FRIDAY
10
Good Friday (Holiday UK, CAN, AUS, NZL)

SATURDAY
11

SUNDAY
12
Easter Sunday

Tufted Duck.....

NOTES

....

....

....

....

....

Tufted duck *(Aythya fuligula)*

The friendly tufted duck was originally native to northern and north-eastern Europe but has now spread widely across western and central Europe, taking up home on both stagnant and freshwater lakes, reservoirs, urban ponds and coastal water.

Suitably named, the yellow-eyed male tufted duck has a wispy crop of feathers at the back of his head and a striking monochrome body with a black coat and white waistcoat. The female is a more muted version of this with brown feathering and no white flanks.

April

Easter Monday (Holiday UK except SCT, R. of Ireland, CAN, AUS, NZL)

MONDAY
13

TUESDAY
14

WEDNESDAY
15

THURSDAY
16

FRIDAY
17

SATURDAY
18

SUNDAY
19

April

MONDAY
20

TUESDAY
21

WEDNESDAY
22   Earth Day

THURSDAY
23   St George's Day

FRIDAY
24   First Day of Ramadan

SATURDAY
25   Anzac Day (AUS, NZL)

SUNDAY
26

Quick- wee- wik........" Quail

NOTES

....

....

....

....

....

Quail *(Coturnix coturnix)*

The petite quail can be resident or migratory and is
most common across the warmer parts of southern
Europe. He keeps to himself and is hard to see
because of his reluctance to take to the skies. His
nature is reclusive and he is usually heard rather
than seen. He has a resonant, ventriloquist, call
that can be thrown far from its source, helping him
maintain his privacy. His song has three distinct
syllables and has led to many anthropomorphic
translations such as 'Wet my lips' and 'Wet my foot'.
Perhaps both of these have reinforced his reputation
as a prophet for the onset of rain.

April/May

Holiday (AUS, NZL)

May

MONDAY
4
Holiday (UK, R. of Ireland)

TUESDAY
5

WEDNESDAY
6

THURSDAY
7

FRIDAY
8

SATURDAY
9

SUNDAY
10
Mother's Day (USA, CAN, AUS, NZL)

"Wi-choo wi-choo ...teechu"..... Coal Tit

NOTES

....

....

....

....

....

Coal tit *(Periparus ater)*

The courting call of the smallest of the tits is soft
and repetitive and his song is high-pitched and
bright. This diminutive but friendly chap prefers
to live amongst tall coniferous trees. As the seasons
become colder he takes on a nomadic existence,
often travelling in large flocks through woods and
gardens on a communal quest for food. He feasts
on tiny insects, nuts and seeds and sometimes stores
his food between the tufts of pine needles for a later
meal. In spring the female builds her moss and hair-
lined nest in a tree cavity, among tree stumps or
ground burrows.

May

MONDAY
11

TUESDAY
12

WEDNESDAY
13

THURSDAY
14

FRIDAY
15

SATURDAY
16

SUNDAY
17

May

WEEK 21

MONDAY
18

Victoria Day (Holiday CAN)

TUESDAY
19

WEDNESDAY
20

THURSDAY
21

FRIDAY
22

SATURDAY
23

SUNDAY
24

" Che-keee........." Kingfisher

NOTES

....

....

....

....

....

Kingfisher *(Alcedo atthis)*

Found across Europe, the rare kingfisher cuts a dash with his electric blue plumage and rusty orange under-feathers, and is dazzling when seen in flight. His song is simple with sweet, high notes that trill in the spring.

Surprisingly petite, he is usually spotted taking a dramatic dive into the water in order to catch fish for himself or his young. Both the male and female use their beaks and feet to laboriously dig out their nest over several days. It consists of a deep tunnel set into the steep bank side, which soon becomes littered inside with uneaten fish remains.

Holiday (UK)
Memorial Day (Holiday USA)

MONDAY
25

TUESDAY
26

WEDNESDAY
27

THURSDAY
28

FRIDAY
29

SATURDAY
30

SUNDAY
31

June

MONDAY
1

Holiday (R. of Ireland)
Queen's Birthday (Holiday NZL)

TUESDAY
2

WEDNESDAY
3

THURSDAY
4

FRIDAY
5

SATURDAY
6

SUNDAY
7

" chir-rr-upp.......chir-rr-uppp........" Skylark

NOTES

....

....

....

....

....

Skylark *(Alauda arvensis)*

Without doubt, the skylark is one of the most impressive songbirds. Poets, artists and musicians have all been inspired by this bird's fast, rich, high-pitched song that he belts out with refinement and ease as he soars upward in flight before plunging downwards, whereupon his beautifully choreographed song ceases exactly on cue. The skylark begins practising his fluid song as early as February and is often up before sunrise, perfecting his melody that only improves further as the onset of spring draws closer. Sadly the skylark is declining in numbers, owing to the increase in intensive agricultural practices, such as the use of pesticides, which result in a lack of winter food.

June

MONDAY
8

TUESDAY
9

WEDNESDAY
10

THURSDAY
11

FRIDAY
12

SATURDAY
13

SUNDAY
14

June

MONDAY
15

TUESDAY
16

WEDNESDAY
17

THURSDAY
18

FRIDAY
19

SATURDAY
20

SUNDAY
21   Father's Day (UK, R. of Ireland, USA, CAN)

" Szeeee ...... seeee ..." Grey Wagtail

NOTES

Grey wagtail *(Motacilla cinerea)*

The largely resident and elegant grey wagtail owns the longest tail of the wagtail family and has black and smoky-grey upperparts with a sulphur yellow chest. This attractive palette contributes to an air of a gentleman. His call can be loud and sharp but his song is made up of chirruping fluty notes and fast trills and warbles.

He is happiest living beside a mountain stream, enjoying the rocky terrain but can make his home in other waterside locations as long as there is running fresh water nearby, from which he can catch water insects and mayflies to feast on. His flight is fast and graceful and he lands lightly with an appropriate bobbing of his long tail.

June

MONDAY
22

TUESDAY
23

WEDNESDAY
24

THURSDAY
25

FRIDAY
26

SATURDAY
27

SUNDAY
28

June/July

MONDAY
29

TUESDAY
30

WEDNESDAY
1
Canada Day (Holiday CAN)

THURSDAY
2

FRIDAY
3
Holiday (USA)

SATURDAY
4
Independence Day (USA)

SUNDAY
5

"Klooo-it.... klooo-it...." Avocet

NOTES

....

....

....

....

....

Avocet *(Recurvirostra avosetta)*

The avocet is an elegant bird with a clear, piped call of high-pitched rhythmic repetitions that accelerate when alarmed. He thrives in small colonies, largely on the east coast of Britain, and is an inspiring success story for conservationists, having almost become extinct in the last century.

He has an aristocratic air with black hood and wing markings that contrast forcefully with his bright white plumage. He can often be seen resting effortlessly on one leg and has a remarkable narrow, upturned and elongated bill. He sweeps this bill from side to side, sieving tiny shrimps and invertebrates from the water to eat.

July

MONDAY
6

TUESDAY
7

WEDNESDAY
8

THURSDAY
9

FRIDAY
10

SATURDAY
11

Battle of the Boyne (N. Ireland)

SUNDAY
12

July

WEEK 29

MONDAY
13
Holiday (N. Ireland)

TUESDAY
14

WEDNESDAY
15

THURSDAY
16

FRIDAY
17

SATURDAY
18

SUNDAY
19

" Chit - chit - chiti - tzerss ...." Wren

NOTES

....

....

....

....

....

Wren *(Troglodytes troglodytes)*

A living adage to the saying that size is not everything, the diminutive wren is a most determined and impressive singer and his boisterous and full-throated warbling song can be heard loudly across the seasons. His song is shrill and is delivered with real gusto.

One of Europe's smallest birds, the wren spends most of his time on or near the ground. A sociable creature, it roosts in groups and is often found in gardens, woodland undergrowth or thickets beside ditches and streams. In spring, the male uses plant stalks, twigs and moss to build a number of spherical nests. The female takes her pick and the new home is finished inside with soft hair and feathers.

July

MONDAY
20

TUESDAY
21

WEDNESDAY
22

THURSDAY
23

FRIDAY
24

SATURDAY
25

SUNDAY
26

July/August

MONDAY
27

TUESDAY
28

WEDNESDAY
29

THURSDAY
30

FRIDAY
31

SATURDAY
1

SUNDAY
2

" Chripp .... tchizzicc .... " Pied Wagtail

NOTES

....

....

....

....

....

Pied wagtail *(Motacilla yarrellii)*

The migratory pied wagtail can be found across
Europe, Asia and northern Africa. He is a busy
character, forever bobbing and 'wagging' his slender
tail up and down as he gives chase to small insects
across the ground. His song is loud and musical and
mixes trills with sweet calls to produce a slight but
nevertheless enjoyable warbling chorus.

He is easily distinguishable and is forever in style
with his monochromatic dress sense. He has a black
crown, nape and throat and a whiteish eye mask
and under parts with flanks that appear to have
been smudged in charcoal dust. In winter his
black feathers fade to a dark grey.

August

Holiday (SCT, R. of Ireland)

MONDAY
3

TUESDAY
4

WEDNESDAY
5

THURSDAY
6

FRIDAY
7

SATURDAY
8

SUNDAY
9

August

MONDAY
10

TUESDAY
11

WEDNESDAY
12

THURSDAY
13

FRIDAY
14

SATURDAY
15

SUNDAY
16

"Tek - tek ... tek - tek ..." Tree Sparrow

NOTES

....

....

....

....

....

Tree sparrow *(Passer montanus)*

The rare tree sparrow can be recognised by his smart chestnut cap and the black marking on his white cheek. His chirruping and cheeping song is loud and bright. As early as February the female perches aloft and flutters her wings, uttering her soft mating call to attract her partner. The couple select a tree hollow and build their dome-shaped nest out of straw and grass. Both parents take turns to incubate the nest.

Sometimes settling in suburban areas, the tree sparrow usually prefers arable farmland where he can make good use of any spilt grain on the ground. Unfortunately this amicable bird has suffered a dramatic decline in population over the last few years.

MONDAY
17

TUESDAY
18

WEDNESDAY
19

THURSDAY
20

FRIDAY
21

SATURDAY
22

SUNDAY
23

August

MONDAY
24

TUESDAY
25

WEDNESDAY
26

THURSDAY
27

FRIDAY
28

SATURDAY
29

SUNDAY
30

" Tac - tac ... tac - tac ... " Blackcap

NOTES

....

....

....

....

....

Blackcap *(Sylvia atricapilla)*

The cheerful hymn of the blackcap, often confused
with that of the garden warbler, begins with a gentle
warbling prelude, which then accelerates in pace
and volume into an impressive bright change of key.
Such musical accomplishment has brought him the
nickname 'King of the warblers', but until recently,
his vocal talent also meant that he was a much
sought-after caged bird in the Mediterranean.

This shy, migratory bird favours gardens and dense
woodlands with brambles and briars, and builds a
rather insubstantial nest that is usually found near
to the ground, hidden in bushes or undergrowth.

August/September

Holiday (UK except SCT)

MONDAY
31

TUESDAY
1

WEDNESDAY
2

THURSDAY
3

FRIDAY
4

SATURDAY
5

Father's Day (AUS, NZL)

SUNDAY
6

September

MONDAY
7

Labor Day (Holiday USA)
Labour Day (Holiday CAN)

TUESDAY
8

WEDNESDAY
9

THURSDAY
10

FRIDAY
11

SATURDAY
12

SUNDAY
13

"Tik-up...tik-up.....pop...." Capercaillie

NOTES

....

....

....

....

....

Capercaillie *(Tetrao urogallus)*

A usually secretive bird, the capercaillie has a
prolonged croaking song that accelerates rapidly
followed by a cork-popping sound and subsequent
hissing and gurgling noises. During courtship,
the male becomes aggressive, and fights regularly
break out between sparring males as they establish
hierarchy and select their mates. The hen looks on
from the quiet of nearby branches before waiting
to be invited to take part in a duet display flight
with her battle-worn mate.

September

MONDAY
14

TUESDAY
15

WEDNESDAY
16

THURSDAY
17

FRIDAY
18

SATURDAY
19

SUNDAY
20

September

MONDAY
21
UN International Day of Peace

TUESDAY
22

WEDNESDAY
23

THURSDAY
24

FRIDAY
25

SATURDAY
26

SUNDAY
27
Daylight Saving Time begins (NZL)

"Wheeet ... wheet ..... tuc-tuc .... " Nightingale

NOTES

....

....

....

....

....

Nightingale *(Luscinia megarhynchos)*

The nightingale is famous for its song, which is indeed of high quality - a fast succession of high, low and rich notes that few other birds can match. What is especially impressive about this is that these avian vocalists are only slightly larger than robins; tiny bodies that are veritably bursting with song. It is so named because it frequently sings at night as well as during the day, which is particularly noticeable as it is one of the only birds awake and doing so. Due to this nighttime serenade its name has stuck for more than a thousand years, recognisable from the Old English 'nihtgale'.

September/October

MONDAY
28

TUESDAY
29

WEDNESDAY
30

THURSDAY
1

FRIDAY
2

SATURDAY
3

World Animal Day
Daylight Saving Time begins (AUS – except NT, QLD, WA)

SUNDAY
4

October

MONDAY
5

TUESDAY
6

WEDNESDAY
7

THURSDAY
8

FRIDAY
9

SATURDAY
10

SUNDAY
11

" Peee..r...weeet .....wheee-er-eee ...." Lapwing

Lapwing *(Vanellus vanellus)*

The elegant lapwing is widespread across the
European countryside and owns a fine head crest of
spiky black plumes that make quite an impression.
The exuberant courting males perform wonderful
flappy, looping 'sky dances' during the breeding
season and this is accompanied by the sound of their
loud, throbbing wings. As a singer, the lapwing owns
a very distinctive high-pitched song that is somewhat
nasal and slurred. His tune is similar to that of a
swannee whistle with flirtatious phrasing that almost
duplicates our own wolf whistle. Both partners build
their shallow hollow nest on the ground and each
take it in turn to sit on the eggs until they hatch.

October

Columbus Day (Holiday USA)
Thanksgiving Day (Holiday CAN)

MONDAY
12

TUESDAY
13

WEDNESDAY
14

THURSDAY
15

FRIDAY
16

SATURDAY
17

SUNDAY
18

October

MONDAY
19

TUESDAY
20

WEDNESDAY
21

THURSDAY
22

FRIDAY
23

SATURDAY
24

SUNDAY
25

British Summer Time ends
European Daylight Saving Time ends

"Ptching.... tching........"Bearded Tit

NOTES

....

....

....

....

....

Bearded tit *(Panurus biarmicus)*

Originally from east Asia, the bearded tit is a
reclusive little bird who spends all his life nestled
in reed beds. His voice is clear but sporadic and
he often prefers silence over song, though he can
sometimes be heard uttering a soft, chattering verse
and the odd repetitive, ringing chorus. The bearded
tit has bright yellow-ringed eyes, a soft grey head
and jet-black mandarin whiskers at either side of
his beak, which gave rise to his misleading name.
He is a nimble fellow, hopping up and down the
reed stalks. He successfully moderates his diet to
accommodate insects in summer and a seed and
vegetable diet in winter.

October/November

Holiday (R. of Ireland)
Labour Day (Holiday NZL)

MONDAY
26

TUESDAY
27

WEDNESDAY
28

THURSDAY
29

FRIDAY
30

Hallowe'en

SATURDAY
31

Daylight Saving Time ends (USA, CAN)

SUNDAY
1

November

MONDAY
2

TUESDAY
3

WEDNESDAY
4

THURSDAY
5

Bonfire Night

FRIDAY
6

SATURDAY
7

SUNDAY
8

Remembrance Sunday (UK)

"Cheeep.... cheeep...." House Sparrow

NOTES

....

....

....

....

....

House sparrow *(Passer domesticus)*

The native house sparrow is a bird we all know and love, and most of us have memories of feeding these perky fellows with crumbs at some time or other. Perhaps the fact that they choose to nest in and around our buildings has contributed to our affection for this bird.

The ditty of the house sparrow is persistent, lively and chattering, consisting of much chirping and twittering as befits this cheeky, mischievous character. Although house sparrows remain as established couples in public, they are also known to have illicit offspring following private infidelities!

November

Veterans Day (Holiday USA)
Remembrance Day (Holiday CAN)

November

MONDAY
16

TUESDAY
17

WEDNESDAY
18

THURSDAY
19

FRIDAY
20

SATURDAY
21

SUNDAY
22

" Swilt - witt - witt - wit ... " Goldfinch

NOTES

....

....

....

....

....

Goldfinch *(Carduelis carduelis)*

Clearly identified by his striking black and red
face mask and yellow wing bars, the goldfinch has
earned his reputation for being one of the most
handsome of farmland birds and garden visitors. A
frequent and repetitive chorister, the goldfinch has a
song that is twittering and chattering in quality with
bouncing liquid trills and a confident final flourish.
The male often likes to sing near his nest and the
tone is lilting and celebratory. Wary in character,
he is hard to spot but his flight is light and skipping
with a bouncy action and, when seen travelling in
small flocks, it is an impressive sight.

November

MONDAY
23

TUESDAY
24

WEDNESDAY
25

Thanksgiving Day (Holiday USA)

THURSDAY
26

FRIDAY
27

SATURDAY
28

SUNDAY
29

November/December

MONDAY
30

TUESDAY
1

WEDNESDAY
2

THURSDAY
3

FRIDAY
4

SATURDAY
5

SUNDAY
6

"Tik-ik-ik-ik ......" Robin

NOTES

....

....

....

....

....

Robin *(Erithacus rubecula)*

The robin's song is beautiful and joyous and is sung
with all his heart and soul. He is one of the few birds
whose song can be heard virtually all year round
and he will happily perform his sweet warbling song
at dusk. In Britain he has become the gardener's
companion, swooping down to dine on worms in the
dug soil and he is often quite aggressive in defence of
his territory.

December

MONDAY
7

TUESDAY
8

WEDNESDAY
9

THURSDAY
10

FRIDAY
11

SATURDAY
12

SUNDAY
13

December

MONDAY
14

TUESDAY
15

WEDNESDAY
16

THURSDAY
17

FRIDAY
18

SATURDAY
19

SUNDAY
20

Pintail......

NOTES

....

....

....

....

....

Pintail *(Anas acuta)*

The Pintail duck breeds mainly in north-eastern Europe, travelling to Britain for the winter. Unfortunately this elegant but shy duck is relatively rare and often hard to identify, preferring to keep to itself in small groups or isolated pairings. In the same manner this elusive breed chooses to move its nesting site every couple of years and as a result is harder to quantify.

This beautifully elegant duck has a toffee-brown coloured head and a straight grey bill with impressive elongated black tail feathers. When seen in flight, often flying in an impressive 'V' formation, these long tail feather stands this breed apart and in courtship the drakes raise their long tail feathers upwards to embellish their flirting display.

December

MONDAY
21

TUESDAY
22

WEDNESDAY
23

Christmas Eve

THURSDAY
24

Christmas Day (Holiday UK, R. of Ireland, USA, CAN, AUS, NZL)

FRIDAY
25

Boxing Day, St Stephen's Day

SATURDAY
26

SUNDAY
27

December 2020/January 2021

MONDAY
28
Holiday (UK, R. of Ireland, CAN, AUS, NZL)

TUESDAY
29

WEDNESDAY
30

THURSDAY
31
New Year's Eve

FRIDAY
1
New Year's Day (Holiday UK, R. of Ireland, USA, CAN, AUS, NZL)

SATURDAY
2

SUNDAY
3

January 2021

Holiday (SCT, NZL)

MONDAY
4

TUESDAY
5

WEDNESDAY
6

THURSDAY
7

FRIDAY
8

SATURDAY
9

SUNDAY
10

2021 Planner

JANUARY	FEBRUARY	MARCH
1 F	1 M	1 M
2 S	2 T	2 T
3 S	3 W	3 W
4 M	4 T	4 T
5 T	5 F	5 F
6 W	6 S	6 S
7 T	7 S	7 S
8 F	8 M	8 M
9 S	9 T	9 T
10 S	10 W	10 W
11 M	11 T	11 T
12 T	12 F	12 F
13 W	13 S	13 S
14 T	14 S	14 S
15 F	15 M	15 M
16 S	16 T	16 T
17 S	17 W	17 W
18 M	18 T	18 T
19 T	19 F	19 F
20 W	20 S	20 S
21 T	21 S	21 S
22 F	22 M	22 M
23 S	23 T	23 T
24 S	24 W	24 W
25 M	25 T	25 T
26 T	26 F	26 F
27 W	27 S	27 S
28 T	28 S	28 S
29 F		29 M
30 S		30 T
31 S		31 W

APRIL	MAY	JUNE
1 T	1 S	1 T
2 F	2 S	2 W
3 S	3 M	3 T
4 S	4 T	4 F
5 M	5 W	5 S
6 T	6 T	6 S
7 W	7 F	7 M
8 T	8 S	8 T
9 F	9 S	9 W
10 S	10 M	10 T
11 S	11 T	11 F
12 M	12 W	12 S
13 T	13 T	13 S
14 W	14 F	14 M
15 T	15 S	15 T
16 F	16 S	16 W
17 S	17 M	17 T
18 S	18 T	18 F
19 M	19 W	19 S
20 T	20 T	20 S
21 W	21 F	21 M
22 T	22 S	22 T
23 F	23 S	23 W
24 S	24 M	24 T
25 S	25 T	25 F
26 M	26 W	26 S
27 T	27 T	27 S
28 W	28 F	28 M
29 T	29 S	29 T
30 F	30 S	30 W
	31 M	

2021 Planner

JULY	AUGUST	SEPTEMBER
1 T	1 S	1 W
2 F	2 M	2 T
3 S	3 T	3 F
4 S	4 W	4 S
5 M	5 T	5 S
6 T	6 F	6 M
7 W	7 S	7 T
8 T	8 S	8 W
9 F	9 M	9 T
10 S	10 T	10 F
11 S	11 W	11 S
12 M	12 T	12 S
13 T	13 F	13 M
14 W	14 S	14 T
15 T	15 S	15 W
16 F	16 M	16 T
17 S	17 T	17 F
18 S	18 W	18 S
19 M	19 T	19 S
20 T	20 F	20 M
21 W	21 S	21 T
22 T	22 S	22 W
23 F	23 M	23 T
24 S	24 T	24 F
25 S	25 W	25 S
26 M	26 T	26 S
27 T	27 F	27 M
28 W	28 S	28 T
29 T	29 S	29 W
30 F	30 M	30 T
31 S	31 T	

OCTOBER	NOVEMBER	DECEMBER
1 F	1 M	1 W
2 S	2 T	2 T
3 S	3 W	3 F
4 M	4 T	4 S
5 T	5 F	5 S
6 W	6 S	6 M
7 T	7 S	7 T
8 F	8 M	8 W
9 S	9 T	9 T
10 S	10 W	10 F
11 M	11 T	11 S
12 T	12 F	12 S
13 W	13 S	13 M
14 T	14 S	14 T
15 F	15 M	15 W
16 S	16 T	16 T
17 S	17 W	17 F
18 M	18 T	18 S
19 T	19 F	19 S
20 W	20 S	20 M
21 T	21 S	21 T
22 F	22 M	22 W
23 S	23 T	23 T
24 S	24 W	24 F
25 M	25 T	25 S
26 T	26 F	26 S
27 W	27 S	27 M
28 T	28 S	28 T
29 F	29 M	29 W
30 S	30 T	30 T
31 S		31 F

Names & Addresses

Name

Address

Postcode

Telephone   Mobile

E-mail

Name

Address

Postcode

Telephone   Mobile

E-mail

Name

Address

Postcode

Telephone   Mobile

E-mail

Name

Address

Postcode

Telephone   Mobile

E-mail

Name

Address

Postcode

Telephone   Mobile

E-mail

Name

Address

Postcode

Telephone   Mobile

E-mail

Names & Addresses

Name

Address

Postcode

Telephone   Mobile

E-mail

Name

Address

Postcode

Telephone   Mobile

E-mail

Name

Address

Postcode

Telephone   Mobile

E-mail

Name

Address

Postcode

Telephone   Mobile

E-mail

Name

Address

Postcode

Telephone   Mobile

E-mail

Name

Address

Postcode

Telephone   Mobile

E-mail

Names & Addresses

Name

Address

Postcode

Telephone   Mobile

E-mail

Name

Address

Postcode

Telephone   Mobile

E-mail

Name

Address

Postcode

Telephone   Mobile

E-mail

Name

Address

Postcode

Telephone   Mobile

E-mail

Name

Address

Postcode

Telephone   Mobile

E-mail

Name

Address

Postcode

Telephone   Mobile

E-mail

Names & Addresses

Name

Address

Postcode

Telephone   Mobile

E-mail

Name

Address

Postcode

Telephone   Mobile

E-mail

Name

Address

Postcode

Telephone   Mobile

E-mail

Name

Address

Postcode

Telephone   Mobile

E-mail

Name

Address

Postcode

Telephone   Mobile

E-mail

Name

Address

Postcode

Telephone   Mobile

E-mail

Notes

125 Fdoor to door frame.
 80 Door width
 90 Door to corner.
─────────
295
 1

A) ~~272~~ 271 cm . ✓

B) 60 cm . ✓

C) ~~107 cm~~ . 176

D) 78 cm . ✓

E) 80 cm . ✓

F) 13 cm . ✓

G) 295 cm . ✓

H) ~~250 cm~~ . 254 ✓

I) ~~78 cm~~ . ?

J) 78 cm ✓

K 78 cm .

Notes

M[icro]ave.

oven. Hob.

Dwasher under.

Door.

60 cm deep.

Fridge Freezer

Dranier

Double SINK

Window.

W Machine

Door.
80 cm wide
80 (2 metres high)

Door
80 cm wide
2 metres high

60 deep cm.
90 cm High } Cabinets

2.3 metres height of room.